onkers

First published in 2015 in Great Britain by
Barrington Stoke Ltd
18 Walker Street, Edinburgh, EH3 7LP

www.barringtonstoke.co.uk

King John and the Abbot text © 2006 Jan Mark
King John and the Abbot illustrations © 2006 Tony Ross

Robin Hood all at Sea text © 2005 Jan Mark
Robin Hood all at Sea illustrations © 2005 Tony Ross

A CIP catalogue record for this book is available
from the British Library upon request

ISBN: 978-1-78112-493-2

Printed in Great Britain by Clays Ltd, St Ives plc

Hook or by Crook

Jan Mark

with illustrations by Tony Ross

onkers

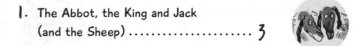

King John and the Abbot

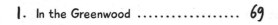

Robin Hood all at Sea

King John and the Abbot

CHAPTER 1

THE ABBOT, THE KING AND JACK
(AND THE SHEEP)

There are three people in this story, and some sheep. And a dog.

The first person is the Abbot of Canterbury.

The second person is Jack Shepherd. He's the hero.

The third person is King John. He's the
baddy. Boo! Hiss!

King John lived in London. Jack and
the Abbot lived far away from London, in
Canterbury. They lived very near to each other,
but they never met.

The sheep lived in a field and Jack lived in a shed at the end of the field. He looked after the sheep – that's why he was called Jack Shepherd.

There was a stone wall down one side of the field. On the other side of the wall was the Abbey of Canterbury. It was a huge house where

monks lived. They were good men who worked hard and prayed to God. They lived like poor men and didn't mind getting their hands dirty.

The top monk was called the Abbot. He prayed to God but he never worked hard. He never got his hands dirty. He was very rich.

People told Jack that he looked like the Abbot. Jack didn't know if this was true because he hadn't got a mirror. But he thought it was a good joke and he liked a laugh. The Abbot was the richest man in Canterbury and Jack was the poorest.

The Abbot had servants and horses and gold and jewels. Jack had nothing but his dog. It helped him look after the sheep.

Jack and the monks waved to each other over the wall. They said "Good morning" and "Nice day, isn't it?" to each other.

Sometimes Jack saw the Abbot ride by on his fine horse. He wore silver rings on his fingers and shiny leather boots on his feet. The Abbot never waved to Jack. Jack didn't say, "Nice day, isn't it?"

Instead he ran to move his sheep in case

they got in the Abbot's way. They weren't really Jack's sheep. They belonged to the Abbot. Jack worked for the Abbot and the Abbot paid his wages. They were very small wages. In fact, Jack was the poorest man in Canterbury.

When his work was done, Jack opened the gate in the stone wall and went into the Abbey church. He liked to hear the monks singing.

Sometimes the Abbot got up and talked about God and Jesus. At Christmas he told how Jesus was born in a stable. Poor shepherds came to see him. At Easter he told how Jesus was sold to his enemies for thirty silver pennies.

This made Jack angry when he thought about it. Thirty pennies was more money than he had ever seen in his life.

Most of the time Jack did his thinking in

the field. He was on his own with the sheep and they didn't say much. He talked to his dog. The dog didn't say much either.

"The Abbot is very rich," Jack said to the dog.

The dog looked at him.

"But Jesus was a poor man like me," Jack said. "I don't suppose he ever had thirty silver pennies either, do you?"

The dog didn't answer.

Jack started work when the sun came up and went to bed when it set. Sometimes he wondered where the sun went at night and hoped it would come back in the morning.

He thought that the sun went round the Earth and he thought the Earth was flat. So did the monks. So did the Abbot. Even the King thought the Earth was flat. Everyone did. This all happened a long time ago. In those days, some people thought the moon was made of cheese.

In summer the sun rose early and set late. The days were long and warm, and Jack and his dog sat in the sunshine and watched the sheep.

"Where does the sun go at night?" Jack said to the dog.

If the dog knew the answer, it didn't tell him.

That was why Jack spent so much time thinking. He never got answers to his questions.

In winter the nights were long and cold. Wind blew through holes in the shed. Rain came through holes in the roof. Jack shivered. He curled up with the dog to keep warm.

Then Jack thought of the Abbot sitting by the big fire in the Abbey. His servants were bringing him hot food and drink.

"We could do with some of that," Jack said to the dog.

Jack didn't know that someone else was thinking about the Abbot. Far away in London, the King had heard about the Abbot of Canterbury.

King John was hopeless with money. He never had enough, and when he did have it he spent it. He was always trying to think of ways to get more.

When someone told King John about the rich Abbot his eyes shone. He smiled a nasty smile. He twiddled his thumbs.

That night he thought of a cunning plan.

CHAPTER 2

THE ABBOT AND THE KING

Jack was fetching his sheep in for the night when a man on a horse rode up to the Abbey. He seemed to be in a hurry.

Next morning, the man rode away again. A little while later Jack saw the Abbot riding across the field. The Abbot was in a hurry too and didn't notice Jack. The Abbot never did notice Jack, but this time it was because he had a lot to think about.

Last night a man had come from London with a message. The message was from the King.

No one liked getting messages from King

John. He always wanted money. Because he was King he didn't have to ask nicely. He just told people, "Give me your money." And they gave it to him.

I wonder how much money he wants from me? the Abbot thought as he rode to London.

It took three days to get to London. The Abbot grew more and more worried. He went to bed worried and he woke up worried.

The King knows I'm a rich man, he thought. *He'll want as much money as he can get.*

When he reached London, the Abbot went to the Royal Palace. The King was waiting on his throne. The Abbot bowed low. The King smiled and twiddled his thumbs.

"Well now," said King John. "So you're the Abbot of Canterbury."

"Yes, Your Majesty," the Abbot said.

"I saw you come in at the gate," the King said. "You have a very fine horse."

"Would you like to keep him?" the Abbot said.

"How many horses do you have?" asked the King.

"Ten, Your Majesty."

"You can keep this one. I'll have the other nine," the King said. "How many servants do you have?"

"A hundred, Your Majesty," said the Abbot. He knew what was coming.

"That's rather a lot," the King said. (He had five hundred servants himself.)

"Shall I send them to you?"

"Just ninety-nine. I won't need them all. Tell me," the King went on. "Is it true that you eat off gold plates?"

"I'll have them sent to you at once," said the Abbot.

"I expect you have lots of jewels tucked away," the King said. He twiddled his thumbs again.

"You can have them all."

"All but one," the King said. "I'm not greedy. But you seem to spend a lot of money. Where do you get it?"

"It's all mine," the Abbot said. "My father was a rich man." He was afraid now, not just worried. "I never spend money that isn't mine."

"I don't think I can trust you," the King said. "I can't trust anyone who has so much money. I think you are plotting against me."

The Abbot fell to his knees. "Your Majesty," he said, "I'm loyal to you. To prove it, I'll send you everything I own. Every jewel, every servant, every horse, every gold plate."

"And every penny," the King said. He twiddled his thumbs like mad. "But I mean it. I'm not greedy. I'll give you a chance. Let's play a little game."

The Abbot broke out in a sweat. This little game didn't sound like fun.

"We'll have a quiz," the King said. "I'll ask you three questions. If you get the answers right, you can keep everything."

"What happens if I get them wrong?" the Abbot said.

"Then I'll keep everything," the King said. "Ready? Question number one. You see me sitting here on my golden throne, with my golden crown on my head. All my servants are standing round me. Tell me, how much do you think I'm worth – to the nearest penny?"

"Can I have time to work it out?" the Abbot said. He had no idea how much the King was worth.

"I'll think about it," the King said. "Question number two. How long will it take me to ride around the Earth? If I have a horse as good as yours, say. And question number three. Tell me what I'm thinking."

The Abbot banged his head on the floor. He

said, "Your Majesty, those are hard questions. I may be a rich man but I'm not a clever one. Can you let me have some time to think about the answers?"

"How long do you want?" the King said, twiddling again.

"Three weeks?" the Abbot said. "One week for each question?"

"All right," King John said. "I'm in a good mood today. I'll let you have three weeks. Then you must come back here and tell me the answers."

"Can I ask a friend?"

"Ask who you like."

"And if I get the answers wrong, you'll take everything I own?" the Abbot said.

"Everything you own and one thing more,"

King John said. "If you get just one answer wrong I'll take your life as well. I'll cut off your head."

CHAPTER 3

THE ABBOT ALL ALONE

The **Abbot rode** away from the palace very slowly. It was a fine spring day. The sun was shining. The birds were singing, even in the middle of London. People went about their business talking and laughing.

The Abbot didn't see them. He didn't hear the birds. He didn't feel the sunshine. He was cold and shivering.

The King has tricked me, he thought. *He knows I can't answer his questions. I'm going to die.*

Why didn't he just take all my money and

*my horses and my servants and my jewels?
I can't stop him. I don't mind being poor. My
monks are poor men.*

*Because he is cruel as well as greedy. He
likes to see me scared.*

*I'm not scared of dying. If I was a soldier I'd
go into battle and fight bravely. I don't mind a
fair fight. This isn't fair,* the Abbot thought.

He went to a friend's house. The friend was
a monk too. He was happy to see the Abbot and
they sat down to talk.

"Tell me," said the Abbot. "How much do
you think the King is worth?"

"Not much, if you ask me," his friend said.
"But don't tell anyone I said so."

"I mean how much money has he got, if you
add everything together?" the Abbot said.

"He's never got enough, I know that," said the friend.

They had a drink and talked about the weather.

"Tell me," the Abbot said. "Just as a matter of interest. How long do you think it'd take to ride around the Earth?"

"Years," the friend said. "I'm glad I haven't got to do it. Why do you ask?"

"Oh I just wondered," the Abbot said. He was ashamed to let his friend know how the King had tricked him.

They had another drink.

"By the way," the Abbot said. "What do you think the King thinks about?"

"I've no idea," said the friend. "I try not to think about the King."

The Abbot said goodbye to his friend and rode sadly away. Perhaps they'd never meet again.

Next day he went to Oxford, where many clever men lived. It took him three days to get there. He stayed four days and spoke to every clever man he met.

He asked them, "What is the King worth?

How long does it take to ride around the Earth?
What does the King think about?"

No one could tell him.

The first week was over.

After that the Abbot went to Cambridge, to find more clever men. It took him four days to get there.

He spent three days looking for clever men to talk to. He asked them, "How long does it take to ride around the Earth? What is the King worth? What does the King think about?"

And still no one could tell him the answers. All they said was, "Why do you want to know?"

The Abbot was still too ashamed to tell them.

People were extremely rude about King John. Some said he wasn't worth a penny. Some said he wasn't worth kicking. They knew these weren't the right answers, but it made them feel better to say them.

Even the Abbot felt better – for a few minutes.

No one really knew what the King was thinking.

"He thinks he can do as he likes," they said.

"And he's right," they said. "He does do what he likes."

"I know," said the Abbot.

No one knew how long it took to ride around the Earth, but the Abbot knew that it would take him three days to get back to London.

I've only got one week left now, he thought. *I won't go back to London. I'll go home to Canterbury. I can't answer the questions. I can't answer them in three years, never mind three weeks. If King John wants me he can come and get me.*

It took the Abbot four days to ride back to Canterbury.

The first morning he woke up and thought, *I have six days left to live. I'm sorry for any bad things I've done.*

On the second morning he thought, *I have five days left to live. I wish I had been a better man. I wish I'd worked hard like my monks, and got my hands dirty.*

On the third morning he thought, *I have four days left. Perhaps I can do something good before I die. I can give away my money before the King gets his hands on it.*

But on the fourth morning all he thought was, *Tonight I'll be back in Canterbury. At least I'll die at home in my own Abbey.*

CHAPTER 4

JACK AND THE ABBOT

Jack was in the field with the sheep when the Abbot came home.

The sun was low in the sky. The shadows were long. Jack saw the Abbot's long shadow before he saw the Abbot.

The Abbot was riding slowly. His head was bent. He looked at the ground.

"What's he looking at?" Jack said to the dog. "There's nothing to see except grass and sheep."

As he came nearer, the Abbot looked up. For the first time in his life he noticed Jack.

Jack saw how sad the Abbot looked. For the first time in his life Jack spoke to the Abbot.

"Good evening," he said.

"It's not a good evening for me," said the Abbot. "In three days' time, I am going to die."

"Are you ill?" Jack said. "You look tired and sad. Come and sit by the wall. I'll go and fetch the monks to help you."

"No, I'm not ill," the Abbot said. "And no one can help me." But he got down from his horse. He and Jack went over to the wall and sat on the grass. The dog sat beside them. The Abbot hadn't sat on the grass since he was a little boy. In the Abbey he sat on a throne that was almost as fine as the one the King sat on.

I suppose the King will want that too, the Abbot thought.

After a bit Jack said, "Why are you going to die?"

"Because the King's going to cut off my head," the Abbot said.

After a bit Jack said, "That's bad news. Why?"

"He wants my money," the Abbot said. "He wants my money and my jewels. He wants my servants and my horses. And I expect he wants my sheep."

"Why don't you give them to him?" Jack said. "He's the King. He can take what he wants. You don't have to die."

"Yes, I do," the Abbot said. "He's playing a cruel game with me. He asked me three questions and if I can't answer them he'll cut off my head. And I don't know the answers. No one does."

After a bit Jack said, "What are the questions?"

The Abbot told him. "The King wants to know how much he is worth – to the nearest penny. He wants to know how long it takes to ride around the Earth. And he wants me to tell him what he's thinking. No one knows what he is thinking. He changes his mind every five minutes. He's famous for that."

Jack sat and thought hard. After a bit he said, "It's all right. You don't have to die."

"Yes I do," the Abbot said. "In three days' time."

"No," said Jack. "You don't. I have a plan. Did the King see your face when you met him?"

"I bowed low and kept on bowing," the Abbot said. "You have to do that when you meet the King. I ended up flat on the floor. Anyway, he wasn't looking at my face. He was looking at my fur cloak, and my jewels. He was counting my rings."

"People say I look a bit like you," Jack said. "I don't know if that's right. I've never seen my own face. But I'm as tall as you. You're a bit fatter, that's all. This is what we'll do. You lend me your fur cloak and hat and boots. Let me wear your rings. I'll ride to London on your horse with your servants behind me. I'll go to the King and answer the questions."

"Do you know the answers?" the Abbot said. He smiled, for the first time in three weeks.

"I may be a poor shepherd but I'm not an idiot," Jack said. "Yes, I know the answers."

"Then tell them to me," the Abbot said.

"And I'll go back to London this very night."

"No," Jack said. "We'll have to do this my way. There's one question that only I can answer. Trust me."

"Very well," said the Abbot. "You're a good man – what's your name?"

"Jack"

"You're a good man, Jack. Tomorrow I'll give you all the things you need and you can go to London. I'll stay here and look after your sheep."

"Don't be daft," Jack said. "You'll leave the gate open and they'll all run away. You'll forget to feed my dog. Send one of your monks to look after the sheep. They know what they are doing."

The Abbot walked back to the Abbey, leading his horse.

He called me daft, the Abbot thought. *I'm a rich Abbot and he's a poor shepherd, but Jack thinks I'm daft. He doesn't trust me to look after my own sheep.*

Then he thought, *Jack's right. I don't know a thing about looking after sheep. The only thing I know how to look after is money.*

He closed the gate. The last thing he thought was, *How does Jack know the answer to those questions?*

CHAPTER 5

JACK AND THE KING

Next morning, **Jack** set off for London. He was riding the Abbot's horse and wearing the Abbot's fur cloak. The Abbot's hat was on his head. The Abbot's boots were on his feet. The Abbot's rings shone on his fingers.

When Jack was a little boy he used to ride on the sheep but he had never sat on a horse before. The Abbot's servants rode behind him and there was one on each side to stop him falling off.

When they got to London they went

straight to the Royal Palace. Jack left the horse with the servants, where everyone could see them. Then he went in at the front door without stopping to knock. The guards thought he must be a great man and bowed low.

This is all right, Jack thought.

He called out, "Tell King John that the Abbot of Canterbury is here! Tell him I've come to answer his questions!"

King John was sitting on his throne. When he saw the hat and fur cloak and the boots and the rings, he began to twiddle his thumbs. He stared so hard at the clothes and the rings that he never even looked at Jack's face.

Who does he think he's shouting at? the King thought. *That hat won't look so good when I've cut off his head.*

"Good evening to you, Your Majesty," Jack said.

"I'm glad to see you got back in time," the King said. "Three weeks to the day."

"I'm never late," Jack said. That was true. There was nothing to be late for, out in the field with the sheep.

"And you've come to answer my questions?" the King said. He thought, *This won't take long. In ten minutes I'll cut off his head and take everything he owns. He won't know the answers, he'll just make excuses. And when he tells me what I'm thinking I'll change my mind. I'm good at that.*

"I'm ready," said Jack.

"Right," said the King, and he twiddled his thumbs. "Question number one. How much am I worth – to the nearest penny?"

"Well," said Jack. "Jesus was sold to his enemies for thirty silver pennies. I don't think you're worth quite as much as he was. Let's say twenty-nine pennies."

The King laughed.

"Is that all?" he said. But he couldn't argue. He couldn't say he was worth more than Jesus.

"All right," said the King. "Question number two. How long will it take me to ride around the Earth?"

"You don't have to ride," Jack said. "You can do it on foot. It takes the sun one whole day to get right round the Earth. Start in the morning when the sun rises and keep with it. Keep going all day and all night until it rises again and you can go round the Earth in twenty-four hours too.

Perhaps you'll find out where the sun goes at night. I've often wondered about that."

Is that the right answer? the King thought. But he didn't know and nor did anyone else. *Still, he said to himself, it doesn't matter if it's right or not. He'll never get the last one and then I'll have his head. On a plate.*

King John gripped the arms of his throne. He leaned forward. He smiled the nasty smile.

"Question number three," he said. "What am I thinking?"

Jack smiled too.

"This'll make you laugh," he said. "You're thinking that I'm the Abbot of Canterbury."

King John did not laugh, but his mouth fell open.

"Who are you then?" he said.

Jack took off the Abbot's hat. He took off the fur cloak and the boots. He took the rings from his fingers.

"Look at me," he said. "Do I look like an Abbot? I'm his poor servant, Jack Shepherd. I take care of his sheep. Well, I answered your question. Wasn't I right?"

This time King John did laugh. He laughed so hard that he started to choke. A servant had to slap him on the back.

"All right," the King said at last. "You've won. The Abbot keeps his head and his money. But I think I'll throw him out of his Abbey and make you the Abbot instead."

"No thank you," Jack said. "I'd be no good as an Abbot. I can't read or write. But I'm fine with sheep."

"Then I'll give you the money to buy your own sheep," said the King. "Go home now and tell the Abbot that Good King John has let him off, for your sake. I haven't laughed so much in years."

Jack bowed low and went out to find his horse.

If that's a good King, he thought, *I hope I never meet a bad one.*

CHAPTER 6

JACK GOES HOME

It took three days to get back to Canterbury, but Jack was used to riding a horse now. They got home before sunset on the third day.

Jack rode over the hill and looked down at the Abbey. He saw the monks walking about. He saw the field where his sheep were eating grass. One monk was sitting by the wall. When Jack rode into the field he saw it was the Abbot.

When the Abbot saw Jack he stood up. Then he sat down again. His legs were trembling.

Jack got off his horse and went over to him.

The Abbot was pale and shivering. He broke out in a sweat. His hands shook.

"How did you get on?" he said. "Did you see the King? Did you answer the questions?"

"I saw the King," Jack said. "I answered the questions."

"Did you get the answers right?"

"I don't know if they were right or not," Jack said. "But neither did the King. I know I got the last one right, though. He wanted me to tell him what he was thinking."

"How did you know what he was thinking?"

"Easy," Jack said. "He thought *I* was *you*. That's why I had to go and see him myself."

Then the Abbot laughed as long and hard as the King had done. He didn't choke, though.

"King John sends you a message," Jack said.

"He wanted to make me the Abbot of Canterbury instead of you. But I knew I'd be no good at it. So he's given me money to buy my own sheep."

"You'll need a field to keep them in," the Abbot said. "I own the field next door to this one. Would you like to have that?"

"Yes, please," Jack said.

"And I'll build you a cottage instead of that old shed," the Abbot said. "I went in there while you were away. It's full of holes and the roof leaks."

"I've noticed that," Jack said.

"I wish you'd told me about it."

"I never had the chance," Jack said.

"But will you go on looking after my sheep?" the Abbot asked. "I'll never find a better shepherd than you."

"I don't know about that," Jack said. "You don't pay me much."

Not long ago he didn't dare speak to the Abbot. He hadn't even said, "Nice day, isn't it?" Now they were talking to each other like ordinary men.

The Abbot looked ashamed.

"How much *do* I pay you?" he said.

"Four pennies a week," Jack said.

"That's terrible!" the Abbot cried. "Well, after this, I shan't *pay* you at all. You saved my life. I shall give you *half* of everything I own!"

"I don't want half of everything you own," Jack said. "A decent wage will do nicely. Give the rest to people who really need it. And you might try living like your monks," he added. "Try getting your hands dirty sometimes."

Jack and the Abbot walked beside the wall to the gate. There they stopped and shook hands.

"I'll always be your good friend, Jack," the Abbot said. "But tell me one thing. Why did you do it? I paid you bad wages. I never spoke to you. I let you live in a leaky shed. But when I was in trouble you saved my life. Why?"

Jack thought about it.

"For a laugh," he said.

The Abbot shook his hand again. Then he opened the gate and went in to his Abbey.

"You know," he said, "you're right. You'd never be any good as an Abbot. You're much too clever."

Jack went back to his shed.

"Thanks very much," he said to the monk who was minding the sheep.

"Any time," the monk said. "I enjoyed it. It was nice and peaceful. Sheep don't say much, do they?"

"I've noticed that," Jack said.

The monk walked away and Jack sat down by the dog.

"Did you miss me?" he said

The dog looked at him. It wagged its tail but it didn't tell him the answer.

"Never mind," Jack said to his dog. "I know what you're thinking. I'm good at that."

SPOT THE DIFFERENCE

CAN YOU SPOT 6 DIFFERENCES BETWEEN THESE TWO PICTURES?

TURN TO PAGE 136 FOR THE ANSWERS

WHICH ROAD
WILL JACK TAKE TO SEE THE KING?

SHOULD JACK TAKE ROAD A, B OR C?

FINISH

A

B

C

TURN TO PAGE 137
FOR THE ANSWER

NASTY NOSH
FOR THE POOR AND POSH

EVERYONE LOVES A GOOD FEED. HOW WOULD YOU HAVE
ENJOYED THESE DELICIOUS DISHES FROM THE MIDDLE AGES?

YUM! A ROAST DINNER WITH A DIFFERENCE

If it had four legs or two wings, they would eat it in the Middle
Ages. Rich people roasted swans, geese, chickens, pheasants, hogs,
deer, boar, goats, hares, rabbits, larks, herons, blackbirds and even
peacocks for their tables. In fact, they went so far as to invent
animals to eat. Cooks would make "cockentrice" — half a young pig
sewn to half a cockerel to make a new and yummy creature!

Poor people were not even supposed to hunt real animals. They
had to make do with what they could get hold of. That included
hedgehogs and squirrels. Tasty.

WATCH YOUR TEETH ON THAT!

Wheat was very expensive in the Middle Ages and so only the rich
had white bread. Poor people made dark, heavy bread from barley
and rye and when those were scarce, they used beans, peas and
even acorns to make their bread. If they broke their teeth on that,
at least they could eat soft pottage — a stew made from oats and
any other bits and bobs they had lying around.

PUDDING

Everyone loves a nice dessert, and rich people in the Middle Ages were no different. They had all sorts of pastries, fruit, jellies, creamy concoctions and sugary sweets such as marchpane — or marzipan as it is better known today. The poor made do with pudding of a different sort — black pudding. That's a mix of pigs' blood, onions, oatmeal and fat, and it may be a pudding, but it's certainly not a dessert!

WORTH YOUR SALT

Salt was very important in the Middle Ages because it was used to preserve food for the winter. But it was very expensive and only the very rich would have put it on their food every day. That's why we say a person is worth their salt.

BOTTOMS UP!

People in the Middle Ages drank a lot of ale and so they may have been a little drunk a lot of the time. Ale was safe to drink, unlike milk, which went off with no fridge to keep it in, and water, which people got from all sorts of sources, including dirty rivers and streams.

ARE YOU AS CLEVER AS JACK?
COULD YOU OUTSMART THE KING?

TRY THESE RIDDLES TO FIND OUT!

1. I will carry you across water, but I am not a bridge or a boat.

   WHAT AM I?

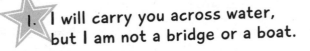

2. What gets wetter as it dries?

3. At the beginning I walked on four legs. Now I walk on two. At the end I will walk on three legs.

   WHAT AM I?

4. What do you keep when you have given it to someone else?

5. Give me food and I will live. Give me water and I will die.

WHAT AM I?

TURN TO PAGE 137 FOR THE ANSWERS

Robin Hood
all at Sea

CHAPTER 1

IN THE GREENWOOD

The world is an unfair place. The rich get richer. The poor get poorer. Many people believe this, but Robin Hood *did* something about it.

He robbed the rich and gave their money to the poor. This was fair, but it was against the law and rich people made the laws. Poor people called Robin Hood a hero. The rich ones called him an outlaw.

When things got too hot for Robin Hood, he went into hiding. He lived in the forest with his

friends and they went on robbing the rich and giving to the poor. Now they were all Outlaws.

They called the forest the Greenwood. It was a fine place to live, but sometimes it was a little too green …

In summer the trees were green. The grass was green, the weeds were green. Even the pond was green.

Robin Hood sat on a tree stump. "I'm sick of this," he said.

His best mate, Little John, walked by. His real name was John Little and he was very large, that was why he was called Little John. It was the Outlaws' idea of a joke.

"What's up with you?" said Little John.

"I'm sick of green," said Robin Hood. "Look around you, everything's green."

"Of course it is," Little John said, "that's why we call it the Greenwood."

"Well, it's too green for me," Robin complained. "The trees are green, the grass is green, the weeds are green. Even I'm green."

"You should wash more often," Little John said.

Robin jumped up and hit him. Little John hit Robin. They rolled around punching each other and fell in the pond. This happened quite often. The other Outlaws stood around and watched them climb out.

They stood there dripping and covered in slime. "Now who's green?" Robin Hood said.

"Fighting again?" Maid Marian said. "Grow up."

Maid Marian was Robin's lady friend. She

was never afraid to tell him what she thought.
One thing she thought was that Robin ought to
marry her. This made Robin nervous.

"He said I needed a wash," Robin said.

"Well, now you've had one," Little John

retorted. "Why are you complaining? *You* said you were green, I didn't."

"I meant my clothes," Robin yelled. "Green!"

"We all wear green," Will Scarlet said. "So we can't be seen in the Greenwood. It's called camouflage."

"I know that," Robin said. "It was my idea in the first place. But I've had enough of green. I can't stand it."

"Some people don't know when they're well off," Friar Tuck said. "We are outlaws. We do as we please, we eat well, we drink deep. We don't pay tax. We rob the rich and give to the poor."

"I'm sick of that too," Robin said.

"But we have to do it," Little John said. "We're outlaws." He thought about it. "I suppose we could rob the rich and keep the money."

"I've had enough," Robin said. "All these people we rob, they've got more money than us."

"Yes," Marian said, "they're the rich. That's why we rob them."

"There must be easier ways to earn a living," Robin said. "Look at the Sheriff of Nottingham. He's got more money than us."

"Not any more," Little John said. "We've stolen most of it."

"What about the Bishop?" Robin said.

"No. We cleaned him out last year," said Little John.

"The Earl?"

"No."

"Wait a bit," Friar Tuck said. "That sea captain we robbed last week. He had piles of cash."

"Not any more," Will Scarlet said. "We've got it."

"He had a fishing boat, didn't he?" Marian said.

"That's it!" Robin cried. "I'll go to sea. I'll be a fisherman. I'll leave the Greenwood."

"Don't be daft," said Little John. "What do you know about fishing?"

"I often go fishing."

"Yes, in the pond," Little John said. "The sea's a bit bigger than our pond."

"Don't try to talk me out of it," Robin said. "I've made up my mind."

"You'll need a boat."

"I'm not listening," Robin said. He started to hum loudly.

"Grow up," said Maid Marian.

"You'll be seasick."

"I'm already sick," Robin said. "Didn't I tell you? I'm sick of green. The sea is blue." He sang, "Hullo, blue sea! Hullo, blue sky!"

"Sometimes the sea is green," Little John told him.

Robin hit him. John hit him back. They rolled around punching each other and fell into the pond.

"Here we go again," said Marian.

CHAPTER 2

TO THE BLUE SEA

Next morning, Robin got ready to leave. He packed his belongings into a sack and slung his trusty longbow over his shoulder.

"You won't catch fish with a bow," Little John said. "Or are you going to hit them over the head with it?"

Robin ignored him. He picked up his quiver of arrows.

"What are you going to do, shoot them?" Friar Tuck said. "They don't stand still, you know."

Robin hummed loudly. "I'm not listening."

"Grow up," said Maid Marian.

The Outlaws walked a little way with Robin to see him off. They stood and waved as he strode through the trees. He waved back, but he did not turn round.

They could hear him singing.

"Hey-diddly-dee, a sailor's life for me!"

"I give him a week," Little John said.

"It'll take him a week to get there," Will Scarlet said.

"All right," Little John said. "Two weeks."

"Two weeks and a day, then," Will said. "One week to get there, one week to come back, and one day in the middle, fishing."

"One day in the middle *not* catching fish," Little John said.

Friar Tuck wrote it all down and the Outlaws laid bets. Marian bet that Robin would be back by tomorrow night.

Then they sat around wondering what to do. They were used to Robin giving the orders. In the end they went out and robbed the Sheriff of Nottingham, just to pass the time.

Meanwhile, Robin was striding across fields and farms. He had left the forest far behind him, but everything was still too green for his liking.

It took him six days to reach the sea. The Outlaws had been wrong about that. At night he slept in barns and sheds. He knocked on the doors of farmhouses and cottages and asked for something to eat.

People said, "Who are you?"

"Robin Hood," said Robin.

They did not always believe him but they gave him something to eat anyway, just in case.

Some of them were suspicious.

"Where are your outlaws then?" they said.

"Oh, I left them at home," Robin said.

"You aren't going to rob me, are you?" said one old woman.

"Madam, I rob the rich and give to the poor," Robin told her. "I never rob the poor."

"Who are you calling poor?" the old woman shouted. "Cheek!" She threw a turnip at him.

"People around here do not understand me," Robin said to himself. He ate the turnip.

One morning he walked across a field and when he came to the other side there were no

more fields to cross. He was on top of a cliff. The
sea lay below him. It was blue.

"At last!" Robin shouted. "No more green!"

He stood on the edge of the cliff. The sea
was a long way down. The beach was a long way
down. At the end of the beach was a little town
with boats drawn up on the sand. Fishing boats.

"Hey-diddly-dee!" Robin sang. He started to walk down the cliff path and sniffed the salt sea air. The fresh wind blew through his hair.

He skipped along the beach. The sand got into his shoes, but he did not care. The sand was yellow, the cliff was white, the sea was blue. There was nothing green anywhere.

"I am in heaven!" he cried.

A man was walking the other way along the beach.

"No, mate," he said. "That's the North Sea over there. And it's nothing like heaven, believe me."

"Are you a fisherman?" Robin said.

"Do I look stupid?" the man said, and he went on stomping along the beach.

On the way into town Robin passed the

church. While he was walking through the churchyard he noticed the gravestones.

They had writing on them. It said things like:

HERE LIES JAMES THE BAKER

HERE LIES MARY THE COOK

UNDER THIS STONE LIES HENRY THE CARPENTER

There were no fishermen's graves.

Someone else was walking through the churchyard. It was the man Robin had met on the beach, coming back again.

"You still here?" the man said.

"Where are the fishermen's graves?" Robin asked. "Don't fishermen die in this town?"

The man looked at him. "No, they don't," he said. "They die at sea. Their bodies are out there, under the waves."

CHAPTER 3

IN THE DARK NIGHT

Robin left the churchyard very quickly and walked on into the town. It did not look like a place with much money in it.

He went down to the beach to see the fishing boats.

The fishermen did not seem friendly.

"What are you hanging about for?" one of them said.

"Do you need any help?" Robin said. "I'm strong and willing."

"What can you do?" said the fisherman.

Robin thought about what he could do. He could shoot an arrow at a target from four hundred paces. And he could hit the bullseye, every time. He could chase deer and catch them. He could hunt rabbits. He was ace at robbing the Sheriff of Nottingham.

"I can do anything," he said.

"Can you splice a rope?" the fisherman asked.

"Er – no."

"Can you raise a sail?"

"No."

"Then you're no good to me," the fisherman said.

It was the same at the next boat, and the next. The fishermen asked Robin if he could do things he had never heard of. No one wanted to give him a job.

The sea was very rough now, the sky was dark and night was falling. Robin was tired of sleeping in barns and sheds. There were no barns in this town. All the sheds smelled of fish. He wished he was back in the Greenwood.

It doesn't look so green in the dark, he thought.

Just then a woman came down the lane. She was carrying a heavy basket on one arm and a baby on the other. Three little children walked behind her.

Robin Hood was a gentleman even if he was an outlaw.

"May I carry your basket, madam?" he said.

"It's very kind of you to offer, but I live just here," the woman said. "Perhaps you could open the gate for me?"

Robin opened the garden gate.

"You're a stranger in town, aren't you?" the woman said. "I haven't seen you before."

"I came here to find work," Robin said. "But I haven't had much luck so far. Now I'm looking for somewhere to sleep."

"I can rent you a room," the woman said, "and I may be able to give you a job. Come on in."

Robin followed the woman and her children into the house.

"What sort of work do you do?" the woman asked.

"I am a fisherman," Robin said. He thought, *She's a woman. She won't know much about fishing.*

"You are the very man I'm looking for," the woman said. "My husband was a fisherman. He died last year and now I'm a widow, but I still have his boat. I rent it to some other fishermen. You look fit and strong. I'll tell the skipper to give you work. Now, come and sit by the fire. We'll have supper when the children are in bed."

Robin and the widow sat by the fire and talked. She asked him what his name was. He decided not to tell her in case she had heard about him. She might not want an outlaw sleeping in her house and working on her boat.

"My name is Simon Wise," he said. "My friends call me Honest Simon."

This was a lie. In fact, it was two lies. Still, people do not become outlaws by telling the truth.

"Well, Simon, I like the look of you," the widow said. "Can you splice a rope?"

"I can," said Robin.

That was three lies.

"Can you raise a sail?"

"I can."

Four lies.

"Can you bait a hook?"

"I can."

Well, that was true. He had caught many fish in the green pond back in the Greenwood.

"Then you can sleep in my spare room tonight," the widow said. "Tomorrow we'll go and look at my boat. I'll tell the skipper to give you a job."

Robin went to bed and thought about his lies. He had never spliced a rope. He knew what a rope was but he had no idea how to splice one. He had never raised a sail. He had never been in a boat at all.

The green pond in the Greenwood was the only water he knew.

Tomorrow he was going to sail on the rough North Sea. He thought of the grey waves

and the grey sky. He remembered the man he
had met in the churchyard. He remembered what
the man had said.

"Fishermen die at sea."

CHAPTER 4
UNDER GREY CLOUDS

After breakfast the widow took Robin down to the beach to see her boat. She picked up the baby and the three little children ran behind her. Robin picked up his bow and arrows, out of habit.

"What are those?" the children said.

"Where I come from, we use them to catch fish," Robin told them. Lying again.

The wind was blowing and the sea was still rough, but the sun shone on the wave crests. The water seemed to be full of sparks.

"This is the boat," the widow said.

Robin had seen the boat before.

"And this is the skipper," the widow said.

Robin had seen the skipper before and the skipper had not forgotten him.

"This is Simon Wise," the widow said. "His friends call him Honest Simon."

The skipper looked at Robin, up and down.

"I want you to give him a job," the widow said. "He can splice a rope and raise a sail and bait a hook with the best of them."

"Really?" the skipper said. "You could have fooled me." He glared at Robin. "You must have learned a lot since yesterday."

"Now, do it to please me," the widow said. "You know you need another man since you lost Ben."

"Whatever you say," the skipper said, but he did not look pleased.

"Good luck," the widow said, and she went back along the beach to her house with the children.

"Now, what tales have you been telling her?" the skipper said.

"Let me work on your boat," Robin said. "You won't regret it."

"I'm regretting it already," the skipper said. He watched Robin climbing into the boat. "Do you know what a landlubber is?"

"No," Robin said. He got his leg tangled up

with the longbow and fell flat on the deck.

"A landlubber," said the skipper, "is a silly

great lump who can't tell one end of a boat from the other. And put that bow out of the way where you can't trip over it."

"That man Ben who you lost – the widow's husband – what happened to him?" Robin said.

"He went over the side," the skipper said. "In a high wind, like this. And a rough sea, like this."

Robin thought of the churchyard where there were no fishermen's graves. He remembered the man he had met. He remembered what the man had said.

"Fishermen die at sea."

The rest of the crew had begun to laugh when they saw Robin fall into the boat. They had plenty more to laugh about during the next few hours.

The men pulled up the anchor and raised the sail. With the wind behind it, the boat rocked and rolled through the waves. They left the land far behind. The beach disappeared, the town disappeared. Last of all, even the cliffs disappeared. There was nothing all around them but grey sea and grey skies.

The men baited their hooks with wriggling worms and leaned over the side of the boat. Robin baited his hook with a wriggling worm and leaned over the side. The wind blew, the waves surged, the boat rocked and rolled. The men caught fish. Robin was sick.

This went on all morning. By noon, a heap of glistening fish lay on the deck. Robin also lay on the deck. He was greener than he had ever been back in the Greenwood.

The skipper stepped over him. He did not look at Robin but he spoke loudly.

"On this boat," he said, "we share everything. We share our food, we share our drink and we share our fish. But we only share our fish," he went on, "if we catch any fish to share."

"Give me time," Robin groaned. "I'm not used to this boat yet. It goes up and down."

"You'd better get used to it," the skipper said. "All boats go up and down."

The crew laughed and baited their hooks again. Robin had not caught a fish yet, so his hook still had the same bait on it. He dangled it over the side. The worm had stopped wriggling. Fish looked at it and turned away.

The Outlaws were right, he thought. *What*

am I doing? These fishermen think I'm a fool, and I am a fool. I just wish I could have them all at home in the Greenwood. Then they'd see what kind of a man Robin Hood is when he is shooting arrows and chasing deer and fighting Little John and robbing the Sheriff of Nottingham.

But, of course, the fishermen did not know that he was Robin Hood. They thought he was Simon Wise, Honest Simon.

When they called him Simon he forgot to answer. He was too busy being sick. That made them laugh all the harder.

"Doesn't even know his own name," they said.

"Simon Wise? Honest Simon? Simple Simon, more like," said the skipper.

Then a shout went up.

"A sail! A sail!"

On the horizon a dark shape could be seen. Another shout went up.

"It's a Frenchman!"

The dark shape came closer, moving very fast.

"Pirates!"

CHAPTER 5

THE BLACK SAIL

The pirate ship was a nasty-looking vessel with a black sail. Nasty-looking men lined the deck. The sun shone on their weapons.

"We are all lost," the skipper groaned. "They'll take our fish, they'll take our boat. They'll take us back to France in chains and throw us into jail."

"Well, what are you going to do about it?" Robin said. He sat up. Suddenly he did not feel so sick.

"Do about it?" the skipper shouted. "What

can we do about it? Look at those villains. They're armed with knives and swords. Their ship is ten times faster than our boat. They'll run us down, and board us. What can we fight them with? Fish hooks? Worms?"

Robin sprang up. He did not feel sick at all. He seized his bow and nocked an arrow.

"Don't be afraid," he cried. "As soon as they're within bowshot we'll see who's master."

"Put that down," the skipper said, "and shut up. You'll have someone's eye out. We've all had enough of your boasting and bragging, you useless great landlubber."

Robin raised his bow and let the arrow fly.

Unfortunately, at that moment, a great wave

struck the boat and the arrow went straight up

in the air. Everyone forgot about the pirates and

stood watching it.

After a little while it came straight down again and hit the deck, not far from where the skipper was standing.

"Whose side are you on?" the skipper yelled. The arrow head was buried in the deck. The shaft was twanging gently.

Robin cursed under his breath. He tugged the arrow from the deck and grabbed a rope that was lying near it. Then he tied himself to the mast.

"We should have thought of that," the skipper said. "We'd have saved ourselves a lot of bother."

But now Robin could stay on his feet and keep his balance, no matter how much the boat rocked and rolled. The French ship was very close now. The fishermen could see the pirates, armed to the teeth. They could even see those teeth, gleaming whitely in black beards.

Robin bent his bow again and let fly with another arrow. This one flew straight and true across the water and found its mark in a pirate's heart.

The villain gave a cry, threw up his arms and vanished. The other pirates growled and waved their weapons, but the weapons were useless and they knew it. They could only fight hand to hand. Twenty pirates with knives and swords did not stand a chance against one man with a longbow.

The fishermen cheered.

"Bet you can't do that twice," the skipper said.

Robin shot another arrow and a second

pirate fell dead. Then another and another. One by one the pirates were picked off and fell dead, hanging over the side of their ship like dirty washing.

At last only the captain was left. He waved his sword and flashed his teeth.

"You'll never take me alive!" he cried.

"We don't want to take you alive," Robin said, and loosed his last arrow. It zipped from the bow, hissed across the water and hit the pirate captain with a dull thud.

The fishermen cheered again and waved their hats in the air. The skipper shook Robin by the hand.

"I knew you were a brave fighter as soon as I saw you," he said.

"You could have fooled me," said Robin.

By now the pirate ship was drifting close to the fishing boat.

"Change course!" the skipper yelled. "We don't want it ramming us. Head for land. Our boat is safe. Our fish are safe, thanks to Simon."

"Hooray for Honest Simon!" the fishermen cheered. "Simon shall share our fish."

This time, Robin Hood remembered that he was Simon Wise. He bowed modestly. Then he turned to the skipper.

"Never mind the fish," he said. "What about the ship? You're not just going to leave it drifting, are you?"

"Well, I suppose we could tow it home," the skipper said. "Maybe we can sell it."

"Listen," Robin said, "what kind of a ship is it?"

"It's a pirate ship," the fishermen said.

"And what do pirates do?" Robin asked them.

The fishermen growled. "They steal from honest men like us."

"So what will they have on their ship?"

The fishermen looked at each other.

"Fish!"

"No," Robin said. "I don't think so. They also steal from rich sea captains. I've done it myself," he added. "Let's board the ship and see what we can find. Follow me, boys!" he shouted. "This is what I'm good at."

CHAPTER 6

THE GOLDEN PRIZE

As soon as the pirate ship came close enough, Robin leaped aboard. The fishermen followed.

First they collected the dead pirates and threw them into the sea. They were cluttering up the deck.

Robin pulled out his trusty dagger and went down into the cabin. He wanted to be sure that there were no pirates still lurking about. Then he led the way into the hold. This was a dark place in the bottom of the ship where the pirates kept their treasure.

"Bring a light!" he called. The skipper followed him in with a candle. The fishermen crowded in behind them and they stood there with their mouths open.

There were oak sea chests all around them, bound with iron. Heavy sacks lay in the corners of the hold. They clinked when people kicked them.

"Bring it all up on deck," Robin said. "Then we'll be able to see what we're doing."

The fishermen carried the sacks and chests up to the deck. Robin slit open the sacks with his dagger. The skipper found an axe and chopped the lids off the chests.

The sacks were filled with jewels. Brooches and buckles, earrings and necklaces and

bracelets poured on to the deck. There was even
a crown in one of the sacks.

"These were high-class pirates," the skipper
said.

The chests were filled with coins.

Everyone sat around staring. They had never seen so much money in all their lives.

"What shall we do with it all?" one of them said.

"I'll tell you what," Robin said, "we'll divide it up. You lot can keep one half and I'll give the rest to the widow and her children. If she hadn't given me a job on this boat we'd never have found our prize."

"Wait a bit," the skipper said. "That's not fair. If the widow hadn't given you a job you would never have sailed with us. And if you hadn't sailed with us we'd be dead men by now, or prisoners. You won this prize all by yourself. You keep the lot."

Robin thought about it.

"That's true," he said. "I'll tell you what.

You take the ship and sell it for whatever you can get. I'll have the treasure. I will give half to the widow and her children, and keep the rest. Then I'll give it to the poor. Those pirates robbed the rich. It's only fair if the poor get what they stole."

"You sound like Robin Hood," the skipper said. "Robbing the rich and giving to the poor. That's what Robin Hood does."

"How do you know about Robin Hood?" Robin said.

"Everyone knows about Robin Hood," the skipper said. "He's famous from one side of England to the other. I'd like to shake his hand."

Robin thought about this on the way back to land. He sat on the deck of the pirate ship with the treasure all around him. He was choosing some earrings and a brooch for Maid Marian.

Shall I tell them the truth? he said to himself. *Shall I tell them that Honest Simon Wise is really Robin Hood? I think they'd like to know. The skipper wanted to shake my hand.*

Then he thought again.

Yes, Robin Hood is famous from one side of the country to the other. He is famous for chasing deer. He is famous for shooting arrows. He is famous for robbing the rich and giving to the poor. He is not famous for being seasick.

And the skipper has shaken the hand of Robin Hood even if he doesn't know it.

He decided to keep quiet.

When the fishing boat came to land, everyone in the town was on the beach to watch.

First the fishermen unloaded the fish.

Then they unloaded the pirate treasure. A great cheer went up from one end of the beach to the other as the men carried the sacks and chests ashore.

Robin went over to the widow, who was waiting with her children.

"Madam," he said, "half of all this is yours. You took pity on Simon Wise when he was down on his luck. Now you will never be poor again."

"And what will you do?" the widow said. "You are a rich man, now."

"I shall give everything to the poor," Robin said. "I don't want to be rich. Rich men get

robbed. I know all about that. And now I must go back where I came from," he said. "My friends will be missing me."

He hoped that his friends were missing him.

Next morning he bought a horse and a donkey. He loaded his half of the treasure on to the donkey and he mounted the horse. Then he said goodbye to the widow and her children. He said goodbye to the fishermen and shook hands again with the skipper. Then he rode up the path to the top of the cliff.

The grey North Sea lay behind him, under heavy grey clouds. The salt sea wind blew down his collar. Ahead of him lay green fields, green grass, and the Greenwood.

He rode towards it and never looked back.

ROBIN HOOD...
REAL OR REALLY NOT?

POETS, WRITERS AND SINGERS HAVE TOLD STORIES OF ROBIN HOOD FOR HUNDREDS OF YEARS. BUT WAS THERE EVER A REAL MAN BEHIND THE LEGEND? READ ON AND DECIDE FOR YOURSELF.

No one knows how old the Robin Hood story is. Some experts believe it dates from the Middle Ages. These experts have different ideas about real people who might have inspired the legend. Other experts believe the legend is a lot older.

The Merry Men do not appear in the oldest stories of Robin Hood. They seem to have been added to the story later.

Many of the real people who have been tied to the Robin Hood story lived in Yorkshire. But in the most famous stories of Robin, he lives in Nottinghamshire. Robin's stories are told in many other places too.

Robin's name does not help us prove whether or not he was real.

Robin is a pet name for Robert, and it was very common in the Middle Ages. Hood might be a surname used by a man who made hoods or hats, or it might be a nickname for a man who wore a hood or a cowl.

Some people think that Robin was a rich man who became an outlaw. If this is true, then he would have lost his lands and his title. He might then have been known by a different name – Robin Hood.

But some people believe that Robin Hood was a slang name for any outlaw – a bit like 'Jack the Lad' or 'Sonny Jim'.

SO WHAT DO YOU THINK?

A   There never was a real Robin Hood —
    he is a made-up character.

B   I am sure there was a real Robin Hood,
    but we will never know for sure who he
    was.

C   I think the truth is somewhere in the
    middle — there may have been one or
    more real men who inspired the Robin
    Hood story, but most of it is made up.

ARE YOU AN OUTLAW
OR AN 'IN-LAW'?

TAKE THIS TEST TO SEE
WHERE YOU STAND!

1. WHERE DO YOU GET HOLD OF YOUR DINNER?

A. I go to the shops, buy healthy ingredients and cook for my family

B. I eat whatever my mum or dad puts in front of me

C. I rustle up my dinner with my bow and arrow

2. HOW DO YOU LIKE TO SPEND YOUR SPARE TIME?

A. Doing chores, exercising and doing my homework

B. Xbox/PlayStation/ online stuff, hanging out with friends and hobbies

C. Singing songs, drinking ale and bopping the Sherriff of Nottingham on the noggin

3. HOW OFTEN DO YOU LIKE TO TAKE A BATH?

A. Once a day (or more)

B. Once a week

C. Bath? What's a bath?

4. WHERE DO YOU GET YOUR MONEY FROM?

A. A paper round or other job

B. The Bank of Mum and Dad

C. I steal it from barons and other rich men

ANSWERS

MOSTLY A: 'IN-LAW'

A real goody two-shoes. You'd be more likely to become the Sherriff of Nottingham than Robin Hood!

MOSTLY B: LAW-ABIDING CITIZEN

You are pretty well balanced. You'd get on fine with the Merry Men.

MOSTLY C: OUTLAW

Mad, bad and dangerous to ... smell! Are you the real Robin Hood?

LIFE IN OLD ENGLAND!
COULD YOU CUT THE MUSTARD?

1. MOST PEOPLE IN OLD ENGLAND CARRIED A KNIFE. WHAT WOULD ROBIN HOOD USE HIS KNIFE FOR?

A. cleaning under his nails

B. whittling sticks

C. eating his dinner

D. self-defence

E. all of the above

2. FOOD AND DRINK IN OLD ENGLAND WERE VERY DIFFERENT. WHICH OF THESE WOULD ROBIN NOT EAT AND DRINK?

A. chicken

B. apples

C. marzipan

D. macaroni

E. barley water

3. MEDICINE IN OLD ENGLAND WAS VERY DIFFERENT TOO. WHICH OF THESE DID DOCTORS USE TO TREAT ILL PEOPLE?

A. leeches

B. maggots

C. toads

D. woodlice

E. all of the above

4. PEOPLE IN OLD ENGLAND DYED THEIR CLOTHES MANY DIFFERENT COLOURS. WHICH OF THESE DO YOU THINK ROBIN WOULD USE TO DYE HIS CLOTHES GREEN?

A. blue woad and red berries

B. red berries and yellow weld

C. blue woad and yellow weld

D. felt tips

TURN TO PAGE 137 FOR THE ANSWERS

PAINFUL PUNISHMENTS
TRUE OR FALSE?

WHICH OF THESE WERE REAL PUNISHMENTS FOR CRIME IN THE MIDDLE AGES?

HAND-CHOPPING

If a person was found guilty of stealing, his or her hand could be chopped off.

DEATH BY FISH

This was a punishment for murdering another person by drowning. The murderer was forced to eat so much fish that his or her stomach exploded.

OUTLAWRY

If a man committed a serious crime or did not come to court to answer to charges of a crime, he could be made an outlaw. This meant that he had no legal rights. Another person could kill him without punishment. It was illegal for any other person to give the outlaw food, shelter or any other help.

THROWING TURNIPS

If a person committed a crime against a man or woman over 70 years old, the victim of the crime was allowed to throw raw turnips at the criminal until his or her arm grew tired.

BOILING IN OIL

For very terrible crimes, people were killed by being boiled in huge vats of oil. A bit like being deep-fried and very nasty indeed.

DUNGHEAP DIGGING

If a person committed a minor crime, he or she could be made to 'dungheap dig'. The person dug a deep hole in a nice big dungheap and then he or she was buried in it up to the neck for up to 24 hours. Other people came along to watch and laugh. At least dungheaps are nice and warm thanks to all the rotting going on!

TURN TO PAGE 137 FOR THE ANSWERS

ANSWERS
HOW WELL DID YOU DO?

SPOT THE DIFFERENCE
(P58-59)

The differences are circled below.

WHICH ROAD WILL JACK TAKE TO SEE THE KING?

(P60-61)

ANSWER: Path A

FINISH

ARE YOU AS CLEVER AS JACK? COULD YOU OUTSMART THE KING?

(P64-65)

1. I am ICE

2. A TOWEL

3. I am a PERSON

4. A PROMISE

5. I am FIRE

LIFE IN OLD ENGLAND!

(P132-133)

1. E

2. D

3. E

4. C

PAINFUL PUNISHMENTS TRUE OR FALSE?

(P134-135)

Hand-chopping: TRUE!

Death by Fish: FALSE!

Outlawry: TRUE!

Throwing Turnips: FALSE!

Boiling in Oil: TRUE!

Dungheap Digging: FALSE!

Conkers